Optimize Your Life Series—
Book 1

The Shower Habit

10 Steps to Increase Energy, Boost
Confidence, and Achieve Your Goals
Without Waking Up Earlier

By Stephanie Ewing

ISBN: 978-1-7369687-0-3

Acknowledgements

To my family, thank you for your
patience, love, and support.

Thank you also to my amazing editor,
Sara Pack. Sara can be found at
SaraPackEditing.com.

Contents

Introduction

Many self-help books have you start with your dream and then make changes toward that goal. It feels great thinking about all the healthy habits, fabulous vacations, and amazing career moves you will make.

The only problem is that it doesn't work. You don't trust yourself to make the changes, and for good reason. Follow through is hard! Don't worry. We will work on overcoming this. Keep reading for a quick and easy fix to your morning routine.

When making a goal or setting a target, we often make the task so daunting that we have no chance for success. Take me for example. I decided that I was going to run a half marathon. Now, did I decide this in my twenties? No, I waited until after I turned forty years old to set this goal. I promptly got online and printed off a Couch to Half Marathon plan and taped it on my fridge. I had two small children at home, worked full-time, and lived on a death trap of a highway directly in front of my house. There was no way to get the stroller to a safe place to walk or jog unless I loaded everyone and everything into the car and drove there, only to unload it, get everyone strapped in, and hope no one needed to use the bathroom! This plan had serious holes in it from the start.

Things that I did not have in place:

- ☐ a set time to walk or jog,
- ☐ a set location to walk or jog,
- ☐ an accountability partner, and
- ☐ a chance in h-e-double-hockey-sticks of meeting this goal.

So, I quickly let myself down and missed a few days of walking/jogging. I felt stupid. Did I really think I could do this? I couldn't even jog for a mile without walking. What was I going to do? Purchase something, obviously. Isn't that always the answer? Still not seeing much success, I bought a used treadmill. And still I saw no success.

Finally, I stumbled into a morning routine of getting on my treadmill every single day. Consistency wins. Not needing to make any decisions was the key.

- ☐ Should I get up and run?
- ☐ Where are my shoes?
- ☐ Did I wash my water bottle?

None of these was a factor because I had already made the decision the night before. I laid out the clothes, shoes, and water bottle and set the alarm. I ran every day.

I did it! On October 24, 2016, I mostly ran 13.1 miles, finished the race, and got the medal to prove it! In hindsight, I was sure that finally creating a morning routine that I could stick to was the key.

Every three months or so after that, I would sign up for a race and keep on jogging to stay in shape. I thought I was set. Done. I had this figured out. I signed up for the same half marathon in October of 2017. Book over. The end.

Also in October of 2017, at age forty-one, I finally got around to scheduling my first mammogram. Then I needed an ultrasound because I had dense tissue. Then I was told that it looked like I had a cyst, but it could be something else. I was asked, "Are you a worrier?" YES. So, I scheduled a biopsy to take a piece of the possible cyst out and test it. Just for my piece of mind.

"Blah, blah, blah ... really aggressive. Blah, blah, need chemo. Blah, blah ... Is that a spot on your liver too? Blah, blah, survivability rates."

That is about the amount of information I was able to take in for the first two weeks after I was diagnosed with breast cancer. (As of the writing of this book, I am three years from the end of my cancer treatment and totally cancer free!)

After treatment, my immune system was shot, my body thought it might be in menopause, and I did not have a toned muscle anywhere to speak of. I thought, I'll just start back with my morning routine that I finally figured out in August of 2016.

But it didn't work.

Wait, what? Why not? What was different? In August of 2016, I had already been working out intermittently for three months. I was younger and healthier and had created a baseline state of physical fitness that was okay. After having a cocktail of drugs designed to kill cells in my body delivered by a medical practitioner wearing a hazmat suit—due to it being so deadly—I did not have a foundation on which to start.

Do you feel like you don't have a foundation? Or maybe you're already pretty physically fit. Either way, we are going to work on your mental muscles, and this will help you immensely.

This shower habit is the magic that created a foundation for meeting my goals. Do it. It works. It is designed to be easy, painless, and quick.

The Premise & Quiz

The Shower Habit will teach you how to:

- ☐ start your day with confidence without getting up earlier,

- ☐ boost your productivity in meeting your goals,

- ☐ reduce stress, and

- ☐ increase happiness.

All by following this simple morning habit. Don't miss this opportunity to make over your morning routine, motivating you to take action toward your goals. These simple changes will transform your life!

You're busy. I get it. You work. You have a family, friends, a pet (or few). It is a lot without adding anything else to your plate, but let me ask you this: Is your current reality exactly where you want to be?

Do you dream of a vacation to the Caribbean?
Do you want to write a book?
Do you want to run a marathon or learn to play the piano?

Whatever your dreams are, you owe it to yourself to try this. You deserve it. After incorporating the Shower Habit into your day, you will have the motivation to take action to achieve your goals. Increased energy and happiness levels will do wonders for your ability to finish the tasks that lead to your desired outcomes. You are not lazy. You are not a hopeless procrastinator. You just need to practice a little self-care by ramping up your morning routine. This process is designed to be enjoyable, rewarding, and highly addictive, so you won't want to miss it!

Let's begin by assessing your shower. Take this quiz to determine if you need to stop reading and make environmental changes or if you score high enough to keep reading.

Shower Quiz

Each question is worth 1 point:

1. Is the bathroom where you shower clean?
2. Does your bathroom have a pleasing scent?
3. Do you have a device in your bathroom that allows you to play music?
4. Do you have a nice, soft towel?
5. Do you have a mirror in your bathroom?
6. Do you have a clock or timer in your bathroom?

If you scored 5–6 points, you are ready to keep reading!

If you scored 3–4 points, you could keep reading, but you may want to consider making changes to your bathroom first.

If you scored 2 or below, stop reading and go make some changes to your bathroom. When your bathroom space can score at least a 3 on the above quiz, then you are ready to keep reading.

Bathroom Makeover

If you scored low on the quiz, I want to help you have the best space possible to complete your Shower Habit. First, let's take it to a basic level of cleanliness. Sweep and mop the floor, wipe down the counter, and clean the mirror. Take a toilet brush to the toilet and wipe off the back of the toilet. Find or buy a candle or something that smells good for the back of the toilet. Now, you can add two points for clean and smells good.

Next, add a clock or digital timer to your bathroom. You must be able to see it from your shower. I guess, if your phone is waterproof, you can take that in, but I really don't recommend that. Phones are too distracting. You can leave your phone on the counter and play some music AFTER you step out of the shower. Now, you can add two more points to your quiz for music and clock.

Finally, the last touches to be extremely ready for your morning routine are a soft, clean, great-smelling towel and a mirror. If you live in a shared bathroom situation, grab a bathroom caddy and put all of your goodies into it—soft towel, mirror, phone, Clorox cleaning wipes, soap, shampoo, lotion, something that smells good, and a dry erase marker.

You have now scored 100 percent on the quiz and are ready to kick some Shower Habit booty!

Accountability

Gather a tribe. Really, friends and family can allow you to meet your goals faster. Call your BFF and have her download this book. Or purchase a copy and have it sent to her house. You can also join a community on social media. Pick an upbeat, goal-focused group and start interacting. Remember, you are the top five people you spend time with, so who are you spending your time with? Are they working toward the goals you want? Hanging out with people who share your goals can increase your accountability. Another accountability booster involves having a checklist. Both friends and a checklist will be the sweet spot in terms of accountability.

If you have a friend who has been diagnosed with breast cancer, send me their email address. What good is knowing a way to help people if you can't share it? #Fcancer.

Start today. This is the most important step. The sooner you start, the more quickly you can feel that dose of endorphins from setting a goal and achieving it! This book is divided into three parts. Part I includes all the necessary steps to engage in a daily shower habit that will boost your confidence and allow you to meet your goals. Say goodbye to inaction and meet your day with a confident kick to the butt!

Routines are not sexy, but confidence is. So get going! No excuses. You CAN do this.

Here is the super weird and difficult to understand part: You don't have to do this every day to see and feel a difference. But you should track each week and give yourself a monthly grade. Did I mention that I work in a school? For example:

Week 1—6 days out of 7 shower habit =	86%
Week 2—7 days out of 7 shower habit =	100%
Week 3—5 days out of 7 shower habit =	71%
Week 4—6 days out of 7 shower habit =	86%
Monthly Grade =	B

So, you are feeling good and implementing at an acceptable level. You are doing it! You are building a foundation of habits that will lead you to great things, and it doesn't need to be 100% to be effective. The worst thing you can do is think that only 100% will work. That is not true. Any day can be a great day. Step in the shower and begin.

Part I

Self-care analogy—your body is the vehicle that your brain, soul, and personality drive around in, so take care of it!

Chapter 1—Shower

> "Just believe in yourself. Even if you don't, pretend that you do, and, at some point, you will." —Venus Williams

Do you want to have more energy? Every morning, do you have time to:

- exercise,
- make a healthy smoothie,
- read an inspirational book, and
- lip sync to your top twenty favorite songs?

Because I am pretty sure that would give you more energy!

But I don't have that kind of time, especially in the morning, so I figured out a hack that makes me feel just about that good in only ten steps. I have included the first four basic steps in Part I, and they only take as long as an average shower. Read on for the first step of this simple, quick method for kicking each day right in the pants.

Begin each day with confidence and know that you can handle whatever stress life throws at you. Together, we are going to design a personalized morning routine that has research to back up the positive gains you will see in your life. You can develop a personalized, energizing morning routine today. Or tomorrow. It's up to you and your time frame.

Are you a morning person? If yes, great! If not, don't worry. This will work for you, too! For this shower habit, being an early riser is NOT mandatory to be successful. If you know that your mornings are not your optimum time, don't worry. You can start your shower habit the second you get home from work. This will still allow you to have high energy and focused time each day.

My approach, and the one that is going to work for you, is to start with a super-easy habit that you may already have in place. In fact, this entire book will feel like one big course in self-care. But the difference is that this self-care is research-based to make physical and physiological changes in your body that will help you accomplish whatever dreams you have. We are going to start small and build an easy-to-follow, feel-great routine. Then we will spend time at the end of this book dreaming and doing!

One important aspect of caring for yourself is to create a morning routine. Why? Because every morning, most people (okay, me) are in a rush and barely take the time to breathe. We are so focused on the million-and-one things we need to get done—children, pets, food, home—that rarely do we spend any "thinking time" focused on our own personal needs. Simply shaving or putting on concealer to cover the dark circles under our tired peepers is not self-care.

We are going to spend at least ten minutes on a routine that fills our emotional and physical bucket. If you have not read Have You Filled a Bucket Today?: A Guide to Daily Happiness for Kids by Carol McCloud, go do that. It's available on Amazon. Everyone needs to take care of their own bucket and fill others' buckets. You can't live your best life with an empty bucket.

Easy Peasy Step 1

Get in the shower. Every. Single. Day. We are going to work on your intention setting and follow through. Think of it like exercising. We are strengthening your brain muscle. This process is not time dependent. You can feel the same sense of accomplishment whether you shower at 7:00 am or 3:00 pm.

Can you commit to getting in your shower daily? As you get into and keep up the shower-every-day habit, this does not mean that you have to shave, shampoo, or even soap up every day. I will leave the specifics of your cleaning routine alone. It's enough that you are committing to step into your shower and turn it on every single day.

This shower will get a little more technical, but step one is simply to shower. Set your intention the night before. Say to yourself, "I am going to shower as soon as I get up tomorrow." Insert the time of day you have committed to if different, and then follow through. This allows you to earn back your own trust.

We tend to put ourselves last, and we often let ourselves down. We say, "I'm going to start eating healthier." Then we go through the McDonalds drive-through—again. Or is this just me? Over time, we lose faith in our ability to follow through. So, you can spend a week accomplishing this first task, and it is still worth it. Set the intention. Follow through.

Take a dry erase marker and write "shower daily" on your bathroom mirror. Then, with that same dry erase marker, put a huge check mark next to that note every time you do it. Then smile, feel that sense of pride, and go about your day. Erase your check mark as you go to bed each night so you can check it off your list tomorrow too!

Home health nurses can tell you how effective your bathroom mirror can be for reminders. It's like a giant whiteboard in everyone's bathroom. Steal this tip from them and use your mirror as a whiteboard for your own benefit.

Now, showering daily might not be a habit that you have. Or you may hit snooze so many times that you create a Warrior Dash to work each day. Leap from bed, jump to the laundry basket, put on clothes while brushing teeth, pour coffee while grabbing keys, and fly out the door. I have a foolproof three-part plan to get you out of bed in time for a shower. But you have to actually do the thinking and create the scene to make this work.

Foolproof Get Outta Bed Plan

First, figure out the thing you would love to do first each morning. Is it pet your dog, eat a piece of dark chocolate, have your neck massaged, have your back scratched? Whatever will keep those eyes popped open is what you are going to do for yourself the instant you wake up.

Next, you are going to keep a journal and pen beside your bed. Write down your intention and reward for the instant your eyes open. "I am going to wake up at [6:00 am]. As soon as I wake up, I am going to [drink an ice-cold glass of water] and then get in my shower." Modify the parts in brackets with your time and your eye-opener.

Finally, this third part only applies if you are a "tough case." If you know yourself to be truly resistant to waking up, then you need a specialty app. Download an app like Alarmy. It is going to force you to wake up and take a picture of something specific (like your shower) before the alarm will shut off. I know, extreme alarms for extreme snoozers.

This three-part process—note something to look forward to, set intention in writing, and use an app/alarm if needed—will work if you have identified a truly rewarding experience for yourself. This is all about your knowledge of yourself and your ability to design a three-part process that will feel like a luxurious reward to you. Maybe I should change mine to fresh-squeezed orange juice. That sounds amazing!

Tips

Showering daily is a required step in this process. However, depending on your hair and skin, actually using shampoo, conditioner, and soap is not required every day. If you know that washing your hair every day would be a disaster of frizzy proportions, no worries. You can wear a shower cap, or just throw your hair up in a clip so you won't get it wet.

If you miss a day, get up the next day and shower. The great news is that people you know will remind you (while holding their noses) if you forget to shower for too long.

Chapter 2—Cool Blast

"Set your intention, follow through, and become your own hero." —Stephanie Ewing

You are already an intention-setting, follow-through machine! (If you have not stopped reading to go shower, do that now.) If you feel like simply showering every day is too easy and won't challenge you, then here is the next step.

Cool Step 2

End your shower with a cool blast of water. You can turn around so that it hits your back or face it straight on.

Start with warm water and keep turning it colder until it feels pretty cool (not cold). We are aiming for about 65 degrees, as anything under 70 degrees is considered a cold shower. No need to cause yourself frostbite here. Just get a cool shock to the system.

The benefits of this cool blast at the end of your shower can include a **faster metabolism** and **increased endorphins**. I have read tons of research about this, but it isn't exactly clear what the link is between cold showers and the benefits.

☐ Is it the increased circulation?

- Does it boost your immune system?

- Does it have to do with levels of brown fat versus white fat and how the cold water affects each of those?

- Is it simply due to making your body work harder to keep your core temperature up?

- Cold water is said to make your skin glow. Is that the key?

The clear part is that THIS works! Go to Google and type in "cold shower." When I searched for "cold shower" while writing this book, about 459 million results popped up in under a second. "Better Than Coffee: The 4 Main Benefits of Cold Showers" and numerous other articles about the benefits of cold showers will outline just how many people are doing this and seeing results! My favorite articles are from lifehack.org and healthline.com.

As you become more and more accustomed to this chilly end to your shower, extend the cool blast of water until you get to three minutes. Three minutes allows you to get the maximum benefit from this habit, no more time is needed for the cool water portion of your daily shower. You will feel awake, energized, focused, and ready to succeed.

Habit Stacks

This process we are beginning is called habit stacking. We began with a habit that you may already have, which is showering ... daily. Then we added the cool water blast. I first read about this idea a few years ago. If you haven't heard about habit stacking, it's simply taking an already established habit and adding to it.

For example, you use the toilet immediately after you wake up. That habit is set, and you won't forget it! To stack a habit on top of this, add squats to your toilet habit. Wake up, use the toilet, do ten squats. This is the beginning of an effective habit stack. Your new habit of ten squats will be triggered each time you use the toilet. You don't need Siri to set an alarm to remind yourself to do ten squats every two hours because you already have an inevitable trigger. *Note: If you are not using the toilet regularly, you really need to look at hydration and talk to your doctor.*

Back to your new habit stack. Once you start the shower, you know you will end with the cool water blast. This process of stacking has shown to be a highly effective way to change behavior. Personally, I still like the visual, so I recommend you take a dry erase marker and add "cool blast" under "shower daily" to your habit list on the mirror. Then, as soon as you get out of the shower, you can put two huge check marks by the list. This is motivating, gives you a sense of accomplishment, and enables you to continue taking the steps needed to meet your goals.

Tip

For the cool water blast at the end of your shower, turn the water to cool and let it run down your back. There is no need to freeze any extra bits off your body. Remember, the cool water blast is about 65 degrees. It will feel coldish, but you can endure it. Start with ten seconds and build up from there.

One benefit that really intrigues me about the cool water blast is shiny, healthy hair. After going through chemotherapy when I had breast cancer, I lost all of my hair. When it finally started growing back in, it was curly! Now, it has a lot more gray, but it's back to its normal straight texture. I really like having hair again! Anything I can do to take care of my hair sounds great to me.

As you become more and more accustomed to the cool blast at the end of your shower, you can turn around to face that water straight on. You can let it stream over your heated skin and think about how strong you are. You have now accomplished two steps of your new Shower Habit. You are a mentally tough shower ninja!

Chapter 3—Affirmations Defeat Nelly

"Create the highest, grandest vision possible for your life because you become what you believe." —Oprah Winfrey

Have you ever heard the phrase "walk tall"? You know, the idea that throwing your shoulders back, lifting your chin up, and stepping with confidence makes you feel ten feet tall. It actually works. You are one of the few mentally tough people who CHOOSE to turn down the water temperature to end with a cool water blast—on purpose—because it leads to success!

Moving on to the gray matter between your ears. My dad used to tell me to smile when I was nervous. He said, "Your brain can't see, so smile and tell it that you are fine, and it will believe you." Actually, that's pretty great advice, even if I thought it was silly at the time. Telling yourself something every morning is a very important part of the foundation for your day.

You might be thinking this sounds hokey. You might be tempted to skip this step. I say to you, whether consciously or not, you already tell yourself something every morning. This chapter is about making those statements consciously positive and out loud.

Before we jump into affirmations, I want to dig into the power of our mind for a moment. A psychologist at Harvard, Ellen Langer wanted to study the relationship between our mind, or what we perceive, and our physical body. The basic premise was this: Does our perception of how much exercise we get affect our physical bodies and how we look?

Her plan was awesome! Ellen got a group of eighty-four hotel maids and divided the women into two groups. For the first group, the researchers carefully went through each cleaning activity that the women did each day and showed them how many calories they were burning. The researchers explained that the day spent cleaning hotel rooms actually fully met the recommendations for leading an active, healthy lifestyle. The second group was not told anything. The researchers took baseline information from all the women—weight, measurements, blood pressure, etc.

Guess what? A month later, when the researchers came back and recorded all the data again, the first group weighed less, measured fewer inches, and had dropped their blood pressure by 10 percent. NOTHING was different. Both groups did the same work. But the first group was told that they were working out every day just by doing their cleaning jobs. Ellen believes that the only thing that explains the differences between the groups was their mindset.

BAM! Mindset matters.

Positive Step 3

Okay, so you have "shower daily" and "cool blast" written on your mirror. Now, we are going to add affirmations to the list of habits. Affirmations help to harness the power of positive thinking. For many of us, there is a little voice in our head that is very negative. This Negative Nelly can lead us to lower our standards for ourselves and, ultimately, stop us from taking chances.

Consider this scenario. Morning sun is filtering through gauzy curtains onto a still form lying beneath a white goose down comforter. The beginning strains of Under the Bridge by the Red Hot Chili Peppers come from the phone lying on the bedside table.

Long strands of dark blonde hair fall across a pale face as her inner voice says, "Just hit snooze again, you lazy slob. That's what you do every day. How are you going to get [XYZ] done if you hit snooze ten times?"

Yikes! That whole scene really took a bad turn as the voice in her head started up for the day. Taking charge of that voice and using that power for your own good is HUGELY life changing. Do it. If the voice in your head says, "You are a failure," unfortunately, we tend to listen and start believing it. Affirmations are positive statements that help us retrain our brain into positive thinking.

So far in this book, if you have followed the shower daily and cool blast, there is no downside. If that's all you do, you'll smell good and be awake! But to take this further, you need to start overpowering the negative and focusing on the positive by creating and saying daily affirmations.

This process is highly personal, but if you need some inspiration, here is what I say:

- "I am strong."

- "I am successful."

- "I accomplish my goals."

I have created a list of affirmations to encourage you. Go to stephanieewingauthor.com and download it if you need inspiration. If you don't want to stop reading, here's a list of affirmation categories that can help spark your own creativity:

- Inspiration—this can be a quote or just words that inspire you (e.g., I am brave.)
- Spiritual—this can be from a religion or based on the energy in our universe (e.g., God is good. I use my energy for good.)
- Personal goal—anything you want to work on (e.g., I am a runner, or I have numerous passive income streams.)
- Compliment—any compliment you would like to have said to you (e.g., I am creative.)

- Gratitude—think about what you are grateful for (e.g., I am grateful for sunshine, a home, my health.)

Now, your goals may lead you to focus on other things, maybe healthy eating, writing, or walking so many steps per day. Whatever makes sense for you, be sure to state it as if you have already achieved it. It can be helpful to pay attention to your negative voice and restate the negative into a positive affirmation. For example, if your little voice says, "No one likes you," then restate that into, "I am funny, and my friends love me."

Another component of affirmations has to do with your mindset. Remember Ellen from Harvard? Mindset matters. Here is another smart lady that you need to listen to. Have you read about growth versus fixed mindset? Carol Dweck, author of *Mindset: The New Psychology of Success*, coined the term "growth mindset" after studying the power of our beliefs.

Both consciously and unconsciously, if we believe we are born with all the intelligence we will ever have, then that is true. However, if you believe that intelligence is malleable, and we can become smarter through curiosity, hard work, and perseverance, then that is true. Our mindset determines our truth. "Whether you believe you can do a thing or not, you are right." This quote is attributed to Henry Ford and captures this concept perfectly.

Tip

You can say your affirmations silently, but the benefits increase if you say them out loud. Repeat them a few times with feeling so you'll really believe them. Your new habit now looks like this:

- ☐ shower,

- ☐ state your affirmations, and

- ☐ finish with a cool blast of water.

That is three huge check marks on the mirror! Look at you, successfully adding these habits to your daily routine.

Chapter 4—Settle on the Breath

"The only way to live is by accepting each minute as an unrepeatable miracle."
—Tara Brach

As you are actively setting an intention for yourself and achieving that every morning, you are changing your brain's structure as new connections are made. I saw it described as creating a path through a field of tall grass. The first time you stomped through the field grumbling about how difficult it was, you were just starting to build this new pathway in your brain. Each morning, as you get up and pass through the grassy field in the same spot, that pathway becomes packed ground with no grass to trip you up.

By the end of a month, you will have created a beautiful wide path that makes you smile just thinking about traversing through that grassy field. Now that you aren't stomping and tripping, you notice the wildflowers mixed in with the grass and hear the birdsong filtering through the nearby trees. You may even begin to crave that walk every morning. It's predictable, beautiful, and rewarding to treat yourself to such an inspiring routine every day.

You are also affecting yourself on a physiological level through hits of dopamine as you achieve your goals! How awesome is that?

PLEASE don't skip this chapter. Practice mindfulness for yourself. This is not about religion or spirituality. This is another way to strengthen our minds. Being present and experiencing our current reality is so important. It helps us in so many ways, yet many of us don't prioritize this.

Breezy Step 4

We are going to make mindfulness easy by stacking it onto our shower habit. After you have completed all your body cleansing rituals and have said your affirmations, you are going to focus your mind inward by taking a deep breath as follows:

- take a deep breath in, counting slowly to 4,

- hold it for 2, and

- breathe out, counting slowly to 4.

Keep focusing on your breath. Your thoughts will wander. That's normal. Just notice your thoughts and let them go, refocusing on your breath. Being mindful and experiencing all the sensations in your body is the basic premise of being in the moment. If your mind begins to wander, just refocus on the breath. Feel the water as it pours down your body. Turn the water to cool and continue focusing on your breath.

Step out of that shower and do a little dance! That is four—count them—four check marks completed from your habit list on the mirror. You have built a solid foundation for yourself every morning. This is the kind of kick start your day needs so you can go out and succeed at life!

Tip
Mindfulness is a skill that takes practice. Throughout your day, take a moment to breathe. Lower your shoulders, release your tongue from the roof of your mouth, and smile. There are so many apps and videos that can help with your mindfulness habit. I love the Calm app and Insight Timer app.

The Shower Habit—Part I Summary

Congratulations! You have completed Part I and mastered the basic steps of the Shower Habit. This may be all you need to do each day to get on track to meet your goals. It's important to celebrate each step and track them daily.

If you cannot write on your bathroom mirror, you can go to my website and download a free checklist for Part I of this book.

Set your intention the night before to wake up and complete your new Shower Habit:

- ☐ Wake up with a smile.

- ☐ Take your shower.

- ☐ Say your affirmations and settle on your breath.

- ☐ End with a cool water blast!

As you complete this routine every day, you are creating a new path in your brain. In the beginning, it will be hard to walk through that tall grassy field in your mind. Each day, you are creating a path that is easier to traverse. By the end of one week, this path will feel pretty familiar and much easier to walk. Great job! If you need a little more support - you can grab The Shower Habit Workbook & Journal!

Part II

Tiny changes in your daily routine can lead to amazing results, so keep reading.

Chapter 5—Pose

"Doughnut Lord lives with Pretzel Lady. She is super nice to animals and strangely was born without bones."
—Sonic the Hedgehog (when he's spying on Tom's wife, Maddie, as she does yoga)

You are a rock star! You have mastered the basic Shower Habit. Each morning, you shower, say your affirmations, focus on your breathing, and end with a cool blast of water. Now, to step up your morning routine, we are going to add a couple of yoga poses.

Energizing Step 5

These are beginner level poses. If you need assistance, you can do these poses against a wall or even sitting in a chair. Add these to your habit stack after your shower.

Mountain Pose
The first pose is Mountain Pose. Start with your feet together and your weight evenly distributed. Straighten your legs and gently flex your quads. Imagine a line running from your head down to your feet. Tighten your core, tuck in your butt, and pull your shoulder blades closer together. Soften your gaze, breathe deep, and hold for thirty seconds.

Upward Salute

Next, move into the Upward Salute. Turn your arms outward so your palms face away from your torso and thumbs point backward. With an inhale, sweep your arms out to the sides and up toward the ceiling. If you have tight shoulders, stop when your arms are parallel to each other. If possible, without hunching your shoulders forward, press your palms firmly together—touch the bases of your palms first, then the palms themselves, and finally the fingers. (Don't do this pose if you have had neck or shoulder injuries.)

Tree Pose/Kickstand Pose

If you feel like you have good balance, you can try Tree Pose. As you move into Tree Pose, pull up your left foot as high as you can on your inner right thigh. If you feel like your balance is not ready for this, you can practice with a modification called Kickstand. Prop your left heel on your right foot, leaving the ball of your left foot on the floor. Remember to keep your body in a line, soften your gaze, and breathe. Hold for thirty seconds. Then do Tree Pose (or Kickstand) on your opposite leg.

The benefits of these yoga poses include improved posture, increased strength, and more confidence. John Hopkins Medicine lists nine benefits of yoga:

1. Yoga improves strength, balance, and flexibility.

2. Yoga helps with back pain relief.
3. Yoga can ease arthritis symptoms.
4. Yoga benefits heart health.
5. Yoga relaxes you to help you sleep better.
7. Yoga can mean more energy and brighter moods.
8. Yoga helps you manage stress.
9. Yoga connects you with a supportive community.
10. Yoga promotes better self-care.

As you can see from the research, yoga benefits are definitely worth some precious time out of your day. For under three minutes, these poses will take your self-care routine to the next level.

Tip
I have a really hard time learning yoga poses from just reading the instructions. I highly recommend watching a yoga video for beginners if this is your first foray into yoga. Also, I recommend taking a yoga class. Yoga is an activity for all ages, and the benefits are vast. If you feel like starting a new activity beyond this habit, this is an excellent choice.

Chapter 6—Squats

"When it comes to health and well-being, regular exercise is about as close to a magic potion as you can get." —Thich Nhat Hanh

Why are we adding squats to the Shower Habit? Well, there are many reasons. Both *Women's Health Magazine* and *Men's Journal* recommend squats daily. Improved core strength, reduced stress, and increased bone mass are just a few of the reasons to add squats to your daily habit. Also, you can do these anywhere, and you don't need any special equipment.

Strengthening Step 6

Just start with ten squats right after yoga. If you want to sneak in some cardio, make them jump squats. If you need help due to poor balance, hang on to a chair or do these against a wall. The variations you can find for squats are almost endless—with weights or without, one leg or both, arms up or down. All have benefits, but here are the basics to remember:

- Start with legs shoulder width apart and chest up.
- Bend at your knees and hips, sticking your butt out like you are sitting in a chair.

- Squat down until your thighs are parallel with the floor. Don't let your knees extend past your toes.
- Pause in the down position with your back straight.
- Press down on your heels and return to a standing position.

You have now mastered the basic squat. Way to go! So, let's review. Every morning (or once per day), you shower, say your affirmations, practice mindfulness, end the shower with a cool blast, step out and dry off, do yoga poses, and then do ten squats.

Now, if you are in amazing physical shape already, the idea of doing ten squats is nothing. I have one word for you—burpees. I will even one-up that and say tuck-jump burpees. Go forth and do many of those, you fitness ninjas.

For the uninitiated, a burpee is a torture move taught to me by my college volleyball coach. Start in a standing position, move into a squat, and put your hands on the ground. Kick your feet back into a plank, do a push up, and then return your feet to the squat position. For funsies, as you return to the squat, stand up and do a tuck jump by jumping up and pulling your knees to your chest. It's really not fun. Do not do this unless you are in shape and supervised.

Tip

Do not forget to dry off first! Doing squats with wet feet is a no-go. Dry off and stand on your no-slip bath mat. You can even upgrade your bath mat, if your budget allows, to a nice cushioned (no-slip) area to finish your morning Shower Habit.

Chapter 7—Massage

Scientist Tiffany Field studied the power of touch in infants. One study found that preemies who received fifteen minutes of touch therapy every day for a week or so gained 47 percent more weight than preemies who did not receive the touch therapy. I think this means that you should go book a massage right now!

Do you love lotion? Depending on your thoughts about body lotion, this may be motivating for you or just "meh." Wherever you fall on the lotion continuum, the next step in your shower habit is a lotion massage. This step is really grounding and can be boosted by affirmations. This step is not for hating on your body. This is a step that says, "I love my body. I love it so much that I am going to care for its largest organ, the skin." Okay, that took a creepy Hannibal Lecter turn. So sorry!

Relaxing Step 7

Grab a handful of lotion and get started on your legs, move down to your feet and really press into those arches and around your heels. Do not forget your elbows, as that area could really use some care, kind of like those cracked, dry heels. Oh, maybe that's just me. Moving on. Take a tiny bit of the lotion and really press into your neck muscles. Don't use too much lotion, or your fingers will slide off and scrape you. Just use a little lotion and press firmly.

Find a lotion that works for you—not too oily, lightly scented, or just shea butter. Like Goldilocks, you need to find your "just right." I personally have two favorites. One is good for my budget, and the other … not so much.

Budget-friendly lotion—Jergens Oil-Infused Enriching Shea Butter at Amazon.com for $7.99.

Other favorite lotion—Caribbean Coconut Goat Milk Body Lotion, found at goldenwoodsoap.com, sells for $23.75.

As you work to select the lotion that's perfect for you, take into account your skin's dryness level, your skin's sensitivities, and your budget. More expensive is not always better. For especially sensitive skin, CeraVe is my go-to choice.

Apply lotion from your feet to your head (excluding your face, as you need a special cream for that). Make sure to get your arms, including your elbows, and legs, including your heels. Remember to pay special attention to the arches of your feet and the trapezius muscle along your upper back and neck. Spending a good fifteen seconds on each of these areas is truly beneficial and highly motivating after you have completed all the other habits in your shower routine.

Tip
Many dermatologists recommend putting on lotion
immediately after you shower. For me, this motivates
me to finish my yoga and squats without lollygagging.
While you are massaging those trapezius muscles,
give yourself a pat on the back for sticking to your
self-care habits!

Chapter 8—Brush

"A smile is a curve that sets everything straight." —Phyllis Diller

When you smile, your body releases three hormones—dopamine, endorphins, and serotonin. That's a fact. These hormones make you feel good. Chocolate also makes you feel good. How do these two facts relate?

Ron Gutman wrote a book about smiling. In the smile book, he reported that British researchers found that smiling creates the same stimulation in your brain as eating over 2,000 chocolate bars! Now, I love chocolate, but I do NOT need that many calories. So, I recommend smiling instead of eating thousands of chocolates.

If you are happy with your teeth, you smile more. If you are happy with yourself, you smile more. If you practice smiling, you smile more. Just do it!

According to the Mayo Clinic, the health of your mouth is more important than you might think. So, due to the value of this step, brushing your teeth gets its own chapter. Brushing and flossing every day are necessary. Did you know that toothbrushes should be changed every three months? Did you know that electric toothbrushes clean more plaque than regular toothbrushes?

If you have questions about your oral health, go see your dentist. Dental professionals can help you determine if your brushing and flossing routine is effective.

A few years ago—or decades—my dental hygienist said, "Okay, today we are going to check the effectiveness of your tooth brushing. Chew this tablet. Now, here's a toothbrush. Go ahead and brush your teeth just like you normally do." So, I did. She came back after two minutes or so, and I was waiting for her. She said something like, "Oh, you're already finished brushing!" I replied affirmatively. Then she brought out this light and shined it in my mouth. "Oh my! What is that?" I had blue-colored crud all over and around almost every tooth. Needless to say, I received a remedial tooth brushing lesson and have benefited ever since.

A Brush with Step 8

Brushing your teeth helps with chocolate eating, smiling, and boosting your confidence. Brushing your teeth is an act of self-care, and it also can drastically affect your health. Now, I am not a dentist, nor do I play one on TV, so here is a very brief summary:

☐ Not taking care of your teeth and gums can lead to a whole list of diseases.

☐ Not taking care of your teeth and gums can also lead to not having any teeth.

The moral of this story is, take care of your teeth. But that is not the entire story. Your mindset when you brush your teeth can affect your overall mental health and the success you experience in sticking with your new habit stack.

If you see brushing your teeth as a chore, you won't be happy when you "have to" do it. If you buy a new brush and get great-tasting toothpaste, then smile about the increased health of your mouth. This changes the whole experience. Your mouth's a window into your overall health. Inflammation of your gums can have serious whole-body ramifications. So, take the time needed to make sure your smile shines!

Tip

I really don't like flossing. My husband uses those little pick-looking things with the floss attached. I am not a fan of those either. Recently, during an online shopping spree, I was reading about neat items in some random article on my Flipboard app. The article shared a favorite floss called Cocofloss by Cocolab. It's a coconut-oil-infused woven dental floss. It's way too expensive, but if novelty works for you, try it.

Chapter 9—Vision Board

"If you can dream it, you can do it."
—Walt Disney

Your very own deserted island awaits. Have you ever played that game? The one where there's a list of all things amazing like coffee, books, school supplies, cats, etc. And then you can only choose four things to take with you to your very own island.

Let's play.

You are on a boat in the ocean. Your boat is sinking. There is a deserted island nearby. You can swim there, but you can only take one bag with you. Choose four items to help you survive on the island:

- Sunscreen
- First aid kit
- Canteen
- Lighter
- Toilet paper
- Hiking boots
- Axe
- Insect repellent
- Fishing rod
- Water filter
- Rope
- Frying pan
- Hammock

- Unlimited supply of tacos
- Coffee
- Coffee mug
- Books
- Chocolate

Now, this type of activity, while fun, can also help you hone your idea of what's necessary in your life. For the record, here is the correct answer—frying pan, lighter, tacos, coffee, books. Yeah, yeah, that's five items. Okay, new rules. You can have five items too. #sorrynotsorry

Again, why are we choosing items for our island? It's to help us focus on our dreams. We need to know our dreams so we can put them on a vision board. Your vision board is actually really important. Many people are not really satisfied with their current reality, but ask them, "What would make you happy?" They can't really answer the question. If you aren't happy where you are, and you don't know where you want to be, it really doesn't matter what you do. Good thing that's not you, or you wouldn't be reading this book!

Our goal is to make your dreams so clear and your routine so pleasant that achieving your goals will be the only course you want to take. The vision board turns your goals into something you can see. This allows you to look at them daily and really helps with the next step of visualizing. You have set yourself up for success. You have proven that you can follow through on your intentions. Now is the time to make your own dreams come true.

Dreamy Step 9

Have you taken the time to really think about your dreams and what you want from your life? If that seems a little too big and nebulous, maybe focus on the next twelve months. Do you have your eye on a pair of shoes, a vacation, a new home? Are you wanting to begin an exercise routine or yoga practice? Visit Disneyland? Pay off debts? Whatever your goals include, find an image that represents each dream and post them somewhere. You can create a paper vision board and cut out pictures from magazines or a digital vision board and paste photos on a notes page.

Another way to keep your vision board focused is to include what you want to feel. Have you heard about the #oneword challenge? It was really popular when everyone was talking about new year's resolutions. There are a ton of resources if you want to check out Twitter or one of the many websites like oneword365.com. Basically, you select a word that has meaning for you. The word becomes your compass, guiding your actions all year. It can help you feel connected to your dreams and keep you motivated. Sign me up! That is exactly what I hope for all of us. This would be a great way to create a vision board. Start with your one word in the middle, and work out from there.

There are two ways to create your vision board. It's kind of like there are two kinds of writers—pantsers and plotters.

If you are a fly-by-the-seat-of-your-pants kind of person, you are more free-flowing and creative. Just start adding inspirations to your board.

If you are a plotter and like more guidance, create a corner for each of your goals. It helps to limit yourself to your top four goals. I like to have one corner for my finances/career, one corner for my creative pursuits, one corner for family/social, and one corner for fun, which generally turns into a dream vacation area and features fruity drinks and beaches!

Treehouse in Costa Rica anyone? Let's plan a Shower Habit Retreat somewhere tropical and go every year! I would love to be inspired by your vision boards. Let's connect and share on my Facebook page @StephanieEwingAuthor.

Here are some easy steps to getting your vision board created:

1. **Brainstorm**—write down or think of all the things that make you smile. Think big, think small. It all gets put on your list. It's even more fun if you have those really small sticky notes and write one idea, thing, or sketch on each note.

2. **Organize**—look over all the sticky notes or your list. See if you can group the ideas into general categories like career, vacation, love life, finances, aspirations, etc.

Generally, it all starts to come together into themes.

3. **#oneword**—as you sit there looking at your thoughts and dreams grouped into themes, what word comes to the forefront? Don't overthink this! It could be love, health, balance, or money. Whatever it is, write it down. Now grab a huge piece of paper and start by writing your word, really big, in the middle.

4. **Four corners**—with your themes/groups already divided up, see if you can further squish them into four general categories. Then designate one corner for each category. Now transfer your sticky note ideas to the paper. You can draw a quick sketch of the idea, print off a great photo, or cut out a picture from a magazine. If you want to do this digitally, then copy and paste away.

5. **Keep score**—leave blank space around each idea. This is the key to making your vision board work! Every time you take a step toward one of the ideas on this board, put a dot, check mark, heart, sticker, stamp, or whatever next to that idea.

As someone who has written more improvement plans than I can remember, I can tell you that the last step is the most important step in the vision board process and the one most everyone leaves out. You must keep score. For example, if you have something to do with health on the board and you just meditated, put a check mark by health! You just moved yourself closer to your dream, and that is worth noting. Mark that sucker and then pat yourself on the back. Great job!

Remember when we discussed mindset? Your attitude toward yourself and the progress you make can mean the difference between success and getting stuck. So, take the time every morning, or once a week, to track your progress on your vision board.

Tip
You have created your vision board. Now, where are you going to put it? On the wall next to your bed, in your closet, right next to your bathroom mirror? This is a really important step because our attention-overloaded brains like to erase details from our short-term memory to keep us sane. To keep this on the tippy top of your brain, it must be visible.

Having it visible also reminds you of the need to keep score. Keeping score lets you know what dreams you are taking steps toward and what dreams are being left behind. This allows you to make a conscious choice to realign your energy if you need to.

Now, take a minute to go do something that aligns to one of your dreams. Then put a check mark on your vision board! You can put two check marks on the vision board if whatever step you took gave you butterflies in your tummy. The steps that seem the hardest often push you outside of your comfort zone, and that is a good sign.

Chapter 10–Visualizing

"We do not need magic to change the world, we carry all the power we need inside ourselves already: we have the power to imagine better." —J.K. Rowling

I almost did not include this step in the Shower Habit routine. This step can be hard for some people. If you are able to master it right away, good job. If you need a little more guidance, that's okay too. I will walk you through the steps. Then I will provide resources if you want to explore further. I have found that the more you practice visualizing, the better you become. Keep trying because visualizing is very beneficial to realizing your dreams.

Visionary Step 10

For the visualization part of your Shower Habit, here are the steps I take and recommend:

☐ Start in a relaxed state.

☐ Take a deep breath.

☐ Think about one dream that you have.

☐ Get very clear on that dream. Include what you are wearing and what you see, smell, hear, and touch. Add all of those to your mental image.

☐ Think about how you will feel having achieved that dream.

Keep trying. Go back to your dream often and add little details. Walk through it all again in your mind.

In 1984, Mary Lou Retton scored the first perfect score in the history of the United States Olympic team. She was only sixteen years old. After the performance, she was asked how it felt (to have scored a perfect ten), and her reply was, "Like it always felt!" The reporter was puzzled since it had never been done before, so he questioned Mary Lou again. She replied, "I've done it thousands of times in my mind!"

We've talked about how important it is to tell your brain what's happening. Remember in Chapter 3 about affirmations? My dad always told me, "Your brain doesn't have eyes, so tell it what you want to believe." The idea of visualizing is especially important in running. Running is really a mental game. There are so many books about this topic for runners. If you are not a runner, here is the cliff notes version.

Create a movie in your mind of what you want to happen, and then play it over and over again. Make sure to add all the details that will make it real—sounds, smells, sensations. I enjoy narrating my "mini-movies" with popular songs. Choose a song that makes you feel invincible and play those lyrics on high volume, in your mind, through your visualization.

I love listening to music. In fact, I listened to a lot of music while writing this book. What music motivates you? Here is my top ten list for this book:

1. Good As Hell—Lizzo
2. Daisies—Katy Perry
3. Nightmare—Halsey
4. This Is Me—Kesha
5. Scars to Your Beautiful—Alessia Cara
6. Lose Yourself—Eminem
7. The Git Up—Blanco Brown
8. Thunder—Imagine Dragons
9. Red Red Wine—UB40
10. Life Is a Highway—Rascal Flatts

Tip

The best time to start the visualization process, in my experience, is right after meditating. Have I mentioned the Calm app yet? I really do love the Body Scan session, which is just guided relaxation. It can be pretty calming in just three minutes, but my favorite length is ten minutes. You can also just google "guided relaxation five minutes" and get a heap of good results. This will walk you through breathing and relaxing each area of your body, part by part.

Okay, we're going to practice. Now that you are relaxed, you are going to visualize what you want in great detail, using all of your senses. Your vision board can be your inspiration. Here are some possible starters for you:

- **New job**—visualize yourself in your new job. What does it look like? How are you dressed? Is there a smell? Do you have anything in your hands?
- **Dream vacation**—this visualization is often easier for people. Hmm, do you think we dream about vacations as a way to escape our current realities? Maybe we should start dreaming up some changes to our way of life so we can be relaxed, calm, and happy every day. Okay, where are you? How did you get there? Where are you staying? What kinds of foods are you going to try? Are you planning any adventures?
- **Running a race**—big or small, can you see it? Are you running on a trail? Is it warm or cool? Is the sun shining? Do you hear a crowd cheering you on?
- **On a date**—picture a special occasion or just because. Are you at dinner? Does your stomach hurt from laughing so much? What do you smell? What do you see?

Some people love visualizing; some not so much. I think if Olympic athletes think that it works, it works. Sounds good enough for me to work at getting better at it.

A short message from the author:

My dream is for this book to reach many people so those who truly need it will have the chance to read it. For this to happen, I need your help.

If you have read this far, would you take a moment to go to Amazon and leave a review for this book? Each time a new book is added to the world of Amazon, it takes reviews for it to be considered a "real book." Without reviews, usually no one is brave enough to try a new author. I would be incredibly grateful if you could take a minute or two to write a review on Amazon for this book.

Thank you for reading and for considering leaving a review!

The Shower Habit—Part II Summary

Excellent job! You have now completed Part I and Part II of The Shower Habit.

You are getting stronger, more focused. You are earning back self-trust. You *can* and *will* follow through. Remember your Part I habits?

- Wake up with a smile.
- Take your shower.
- Say your affirmations and settle on your breath.
- End with a cool water blast!

You have now added six more steps to those!

- Find your Zen through a few yoga poses.
- Strengthen your body and balance with squats.
- Take care of your teeth to boost confidence.
- Massage with lotion for glowing skin.
- Create a visible scoreboard for your dreams.
- Visualize your best life every day.

Keep stepping into that shower and triggering your habit stack. These actions will kickstart your new chapter of self-care and lead to a massive boost of energy. Use it wisely!

Part III

Crystal clear dreams … successful daily Shower Habit … The possibilities of where you go next are limitless.

Chapter 11—Start Where You Are

"Success is not the way to happiness.
Happiness is the way to success."
—Albert Schweitzer

Wherever you are right now is where you are meant to be. Where you are tomorrow … Well, that's up to your imagination and willingness to act. The Shower Habit walks you through ten steps to create a powerful morning routine designed to boost your confidence and energy. Now, take these gifts of energy and confidence and put them to good use. You have what it takes to reach your goals.

Charlie "Tremendous" Jones said, "You will be the same person in five years as you are today except for the people you meet and the books you read." Look at you, reading books to boost your energy and confidence so you can achieve anything!

Now, go look at that vision board and add another tally to your score. Keep it up. Meet new people who share your goals, and keep reading. As you change, your goals will evolve. That's great! Update your vision board and keep stepping into that shower every morning, knowing that you are going to end with a cool water blast. Why? Because it's good for you and you are worth it.

Chapter 12—Life Goals

"You will never change your life until you
change something that you do daily."
—John Maxwell

What are you going to commit to doing daily? Take some time to reflect. Track your progress for a week. It will become clear what parts of the Shower Habit really resonate with you. This needs to feel like self-care to YOU. You decide what to keep and what to let go of. No matter what steps you decide to keep, if you believe that you have created your ultimate morning routine, it will provide you with great benefits. The power of your thoughts is huge!

From the great Lewis Carroll's *Through the Looking Glass* comes the wisdom of practice, and one should always believe a mad queen.

"I can't believe that!" said Alice.

"Can't you?" the Queen said in a pitying tone. "Try again: draw a long breath, and shut your eyes."

Alice laughed. "There's no use trying," she said, "one can't believe impossible things."

"I daresay you haven't had much practice," said the Queen. "When I was your age, I always did it for half-an-hour a day. Why, sometimes I've believed as many as six impossible things before breakfast."

The Shower Habit is not impossible. Tailor it to your life and then be consistent. No one is perfect, but consistency over time can lead to amazing results!

Essential Books for Life Goals

You need to have a personal goal or dream that you are working toward. Successful people read and learn from a lot of people. If you already have a goal in mind, find a book on that topic and purchase it. If you need help setting a personal goal, here is my list to get you started:

- On the topic of finances, I recommend *The Total Money Makeover* by Dave Ramsey. The Baby Steps that he outlines in his book stepped me right outta debt and into a much more serene state of life. It is amazing the weight that you carry when you are worried about making payments every month. It's even worse when you are still actively creating debt while at the same time worrying about it.

- On the topic of sales, I recommend Hal Elrod and his *Miracle Morning for Salespeople*. Just get in the right frame of mind and jump into the deep end of this book.

- On the topic of confidence, I recommend *You Are a Badass* by Jen Sincero. This book tends to polarize people into the "I hate" or "I love" camps. I am wholeheartedly in the "I love" camp. Put on your tennis shoes, go for a walk, and listen to Jen motivate you in the audio book.

☐ On the topic of writing, I have two recommendations that I cannot decide between because they are so different. Gundi Gabrielle wrote *Kindle Bestseller Publishing: Publish a Bestseller in the next 30 Days!* I read Gundi's book after I read *So You Want to Be a Writer: How to get started (while you still have a day job)* by Allison Tait and Valerie Khoo. Both of these books together were the kick in the butt that I needed to finally make one of my dreams the reality that you are reading right now.

One of my best friends has a sign hanging in her office that reads, "A kick in the butt is a step forward." Anonymous.

I hope this book feels less like a kick and way more like a gentle nudge. You can do it! I know you can.

"Go confidently in the direction of your dreams. Live the life you've imagined."
—Henry David Thoreau

Shopping list

Here is your one-stop shop for items mentioned in this book:

- Apps
  - Calm App
  - Insight Timer
  - Alarmy

- Other items
  - Lotions—CeraVe, Jergens, Goatmilk Lotion
  - Floss—Cocolab
  - Dry erase markers
  - Non-slip cushioned bath mat

Letter from the Author

Did you like the Shower Habit? Was it helpful? How many days have you completed your Shower Habit? What goals have you achieved? Did you post a photo of your vision board on Facebook? I would love to hear from you. The thing that makes authors the happiest is reviews of our books. Do you like it? Do you want to read about sleep habits next?

If you can take a minute to leave a review on Amazon, I would be very grateful. I have also created a Shower Habit Workbook and Journal to support this new habit.

If you want to know when the next book is coming out, visit stephanieewingauthor.com to leave me your email address. And follow me on Facebook @StephanieEwingAuthor.

Thanks for reading!

Stephanie

Sneak Peek into *The Sleep Habit*

Introduction

Up until I began my chosen career path, I slept great. In college, I was playing volleyball, getting good grades, working, and going to school at night, and I was able to sleep pretty darn well. And I LOVE to sleep. Give me my comfy bed and even comfier body pillow (seriously, why do they not become a thing until pregnancy?), and I will sleep in like a teenager!

However, I have developed quite the problem falling asleep. What should I do? Medication? "Oh, by the way, this is highly addictive." No thank you.

Well, maybe. It really depends on how many nights it's been since I felt like I slept.

Did you know that not sleeping is actually a great way to drive yourself insane? No really, serious torture techniques involve no sleep. Prisoners can't tell what's reality. It's pretty horrible stuff. Don't google that.

Okay, so now that you're back from that rabbit hole (I warned you!), what can you do to develop good sleep habits? Well, you can go talk to your medical doctor, or you can go talk to a therapist.

I actually recommend both of those steps. I also want to give you a step-by-step guide to follow *in addition to* the professional help that I recommended above. When you are not sleeping well, complicated stuff does not make sense. Easy things seem as complicated as preparing to climb Mt. Everest, so why try? Here are some simple, easy-to-take steps that cost very little money and can totally revamp your sleep habits in just three days. Seriously.

However, this isn't a choose-your-own adventure guide. You will need to actually act on every step. If there are choices, I will let you know. Otherwise, EVERY step must happen.

Mindset

Ok, I really hope you have read *The Shower Habit* because this will make so much more sense if you have. However, if you haven't, I will break it down for you here:

- ☐ Mindset matters.
- ☐ Read about Carol Dweck.
- ☐ Your belief is your truth.

Carol Dweck coined the term "growth mindset" to describe people who believe that with hard work and perseverance, you can learn and grow.

This will work if you follow the steps, even talking to your doctor and therapist, and you *believe* it will work. If you are a serious skeptic, no worries. Your homework is to take the quiz. Make ALL the changes suggested. Read this book once and put it away for a week. Then re-read the book and follow every step. Your mind has to see the possibilities before you begin. This technique of giving yourself time to process the information will help with most habits that you want to start. You just need time to convince your brain that this can work. Get your Negative Nelly inner voice on board and go for it!

To make this easier to implement, I have divided this book into three parts. Parts I and III are super easy to implement. Like most things in life, though, the easy changes are not where the most growth happens. Part II is the magic of your new and improved sleep habit. This is not going to be easy, but it is simple and will make a huge difference in your quality and quantity of sleep.

Importance of Sleep
Sleep is really important for health and being on top of your game. Attention, problem solving, and reflexes are all tied to getting enough sleep. Also, a lack of sleep is tied to numerous health conditions like obesity, type 2 diabetes, high blood pressure, heart disease, stroke, poor mental health, and even early death. Yikes! Early death is not something we need, so get good sleep by implementing effective routines.

Chapter 1—Food List

There are four main vitamins and minerals found in food that aid in promoting sleep—tryptophan, magnesium, calcium, and B6. Let's be really clear. I am not a doctor, nor do I play one on TV. You should talk to your doctor about adding to or changing your diet. The entire point of this book is to help you feel better. Your doctor needs to be part of that wellness team. You need to be an educated part of that team, and this book is one component to help you get educated about you.

Tryptophan and B6
Tryptophan is an amino acid found in many foods that can help your body make the hormone melatonin. Tryptophan is used by the body to make serotonin, and it is then turned into melatonin.

However, if you are low in B6, your body has a harder time turning tryptophan into melatonin. So, in order for your body to do this efficiently, you need B6. Read through the following lists and then go stock up on a few of these items.

- Foods containing Tryptophan:

    - Dairy—milk, cheese, yogurt

    - Fruits—apples, peaches, bananas, avocados

- [ ] Seeds—pumpkin, sesame, sunflower, flax,

- [ ] Nuts—walnuts, almonds, peanuts, cashews

- [ ] Vegetables—broccoli, spinach, asparagus, onion

- [ ] Seafood and poultry—tuna, shrimp, salmon, sardines, cod, turkey, chicken

- [ ] Foods containing B6 (remember, your body needs B6 to help convert tryptophan):

  - [ ] Seeds—sunflower, flax,

  - [ ] Nuts—pistachio

  - [ ] Seafood and meat—tuna, salmon, halibut, chicken, pork, beef

  - [ ] Fruit—banana, avocado, dried prunes

  - [ ] Vegetables—spinach

Magnesium
This is a mineral that naturally relaxes the body. It actually helps deactivate adrenaline. I need that on hand right after my kids jump out and try to scare me before bed! Or maybe I need to feed it to my kids and husband when I hide in their dark bedrooms and jump out to scare them. Whatever. It's because I love them.

- [ ] Foods containing Magnesium:

  - [ ] Dairy—yogurt

- Seeds—sunflower, flax

- Nuts—cashews, brazil nuts, pecans

- Fruits—bananas, avocados

- Vegetables—baby spinach, kale, dark leafy greens

- Seafood—salmon, halibut, tuna, mackerel

Calcium

Calcium also helps your body make melatonin. Remember, making melatonin is good, as this hormone helps you get to sleep and stay asleep.

- Foods containing Calcium:

  - Dairy—milk, cheese, yogurt

  - Vegetables—green snap peas, okra, broccoli

  - Seafood—sardines

Melatonin

Now that we have covered all the foods that can help your body with sleep, primarily by being turned into melatonin, we will look at the foods that are excellent sources of naturally occurring melatonin.

- Foods containing melatonin:

  - Seeds—sunflower, mustard, flax

  - Nuts—walnuts, peanuts

- Fruits—tart cherries, pomegranate, grapes, tomatoes

- Vegetables—corn, asparagus, olives, broccoli, cucumber

Based on that entire list of foods that will help me sleep, I am thinking a nice yogurt with cherries, walnuts, and sunflower seeds might be the perfect evening food. Only problem is most yogurt has way too much sugar. So maybe a trail mix of walnuts, peanuts, sunflower seeds, cherries, and dried prunes. Or try these melatonin-rich dinner ideas:

- Sleepy Food Meals

  - Salmon, asparagus

  - Almond-crusted halibut with tomato, onion, cucumber salad

  - Cheddar broccoli soup

  - Tuna avocado melt

  - Pomegranate avocado toast

  - Caramelized onion and cherry tartine

That's all for now. Grab your copy of
The Sleep Habit
on Amazon.

You can also get The Shower Habit Workbook & Journal on Amazon!

Made in the USA
Monee, IL
19 March 2023